More Adventures of the SUPERKIDS

STUDENT BOOK UNITS 1–2

Name

THE SUPERKIDS READING PROGRAM

FIRST GRADE

More Adventures of the
SUPERKIDS

BY PLEASANT T. ROWLAND

ILLUSTRATED BY LORETTA LUSTIG, MERYL HENDERSON & DOUG ROY

CONTRIBUTING WRITER: VALERIE TRIPP

DEVELOPED BY ROWLAND READING FOUNDATION

For the convenience of teachers and parents, this book contains abbreviated citations of the Common Core State Standards, noted in pink at the bottom of each page. The complete standards are available online at *superkidsreading.org*.

ISBN: 978-1-61436-225-8   MO36225.0315   2 3 4 5 6 4495 19 18 17 16 15

UNITS   1–2   3–4   5–6   7–8   9–10

Unit 1

⭐ Y can be a vowel.

Y can stand for ī.　　bȳ　　mȳ

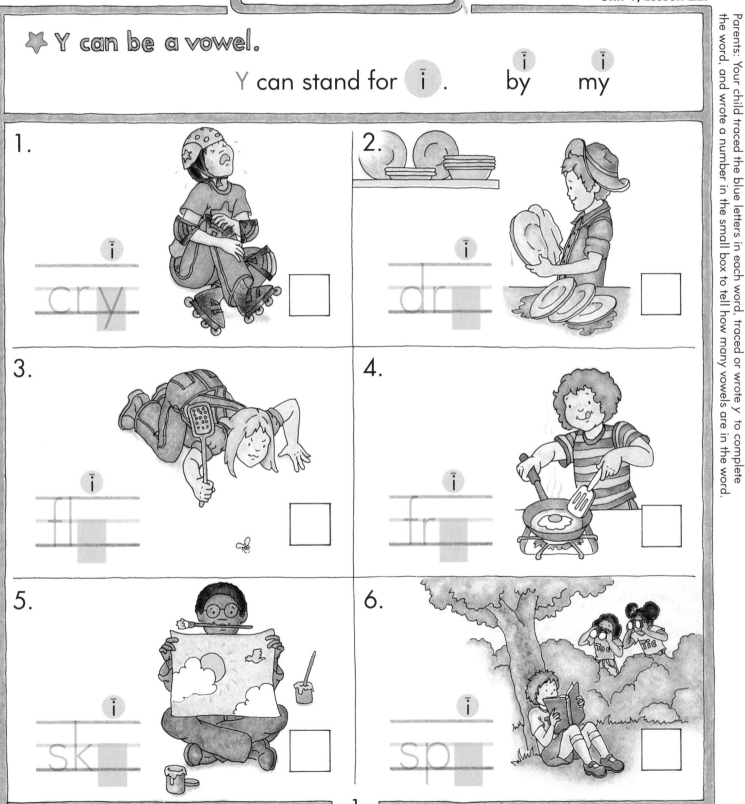

1. cry

2. dr___

3. fl___

4. fr___

5. sk___

6. sp___

1

⭐ When a word ends in y and it's the only vowel, the y stands for the long i sound.

Phonemic Awareness, Phonics
RF.1.2, RF.1.3, RF.1.3b, RF.1.3d

Parents: Your child traced the blue letters in each word, traced or wrote y to complete the word, and wrote a number in the small box to tell how many vowels are in the word.

⭐ **Y can be a vowel.**

Y can stand for ē .   happy ē   silly ē

1.
ē
puppy ☐

2.
ē
bunn__ ☐

3.
ē
__ck__ ☐

4.
ē
jell__ ☐

5.
ē
penn__ ☐

6.
ē
cand__ ☐

Parents: Your child traced the blue letters in each word, traced or wrote y to complete the word, and wrote a number in the small box to tell how many vowels are in the word. Then your child drew a line from the word to the part of the picture it describes.

2

⭐ When a word ends in y and has another vowel that is not next to it, the y stands for the long e sound.

Phonemic Awareness, Phonics
RF.1.2, RF.1.3, RF.1.3b, RF.1.3d

1. ☐ fry   ē   ī

2. ☐ hungry   ē   ī

3. ☐ cry   ē   ī

4. ☐ dry   ē   ī

5. ☐ messy   ē   ī

6. ☐ fifty   ē   ī

7. ☐ itchy   ē   ī

8. ☐ sandy   ē   ī

9. ☐ bunny   ē   ī

10. ☐ silly   ē   ī

Parents: In the small box by each word, your child wrote a number to tell how many vowels are in the word. Then your child circled ē or ī to tell which sound y stands for in the word and drew a line from the word to the picture it describes.

Phonics
RF.1.2, RF.1.3b, RF.1.3d

Unit 1, Lesson 228

1.

plāy̶

2.

clay

3.

tray

4.

$1.75

Show for Kids!

pay

5.

dāy

6.

spray

Parents: Your child marked the a in each word as standing for the long-vowel sound and crossed out the y to show it's silent.

4

When a word has two vowels together, the first is usually long and the second is silent.

Phonemic Awareness, Phonics
RF.1.2d, RF.1.3c, RF.1.3b

Memory Words

down   too   work   many   first

 Look at the rain come down!

 What a yucky, drizzly day!

 Oh, don't be so grumpy.
There are lots of games to play!

 I want to work on monster masks.

 I want to make a mask, too.

 How many kids want to make leaf prints?

 That is a fun thing to do.

 First, let's play leapfrog!
Come on! Let's stand in a line.

 I will make a raincoat for my doll,
with a hat and boots like mine.

 When the sky is gray and weepy,
it just makes me very sleepy.

down

too

work

many

first

Pattern Words

___y
- by
- fly
- try

___elly
- belly
- jelly
- smelly

___unny
- bunny
- funny
- sunny

___ay
- may
- say
- play

down   too   work   many   first

Rain comes down,
drizzle, too.
But there is still
a lot to do.
Play or work,
stay inside.
Think up many
games to try.
So at first
you may be mad.
But rainy days
are not too bad.

6

Vocabulary, Spelling
L.1.4, L.1.2d, L.1.2e

Parents: Your child completed each sentence by writing on the handwriting lines the Memory Word from the top of the page that makes sense in the sentence.

down   too   work   many   First

1. The Superkids like to _____ on projects when it rains.

2. _____ , the kids made monster masks.

3. Then the kids hopped _____ a leapfrog line.

4. Sal tossed _____ beanbags to feed the dragon.

5. Toc napped. Icky napped, _____ .

7

Leaf Prints

Leapfrog

Odd Socks

Parents: Your child drew a line to connect each project name on pages 8 and 9 with the materials needed for the project in the first row of pictures and the completed project in the last row.

A Monster Mask

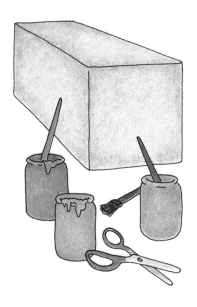

A Dragon for a Game

A Doll's Rain Suit

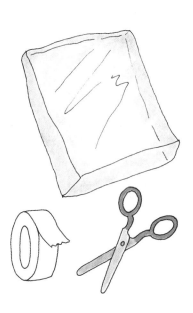

Comprehension
RI.1.2, RL.1.7

Here are two ways to spell ā: ai and ay.
Use ai in the middle. Use ay at the end.

1.

sail   pay

2.

sn___l   spr___ ___

3.

r___n   pl___ ___

4.

t___ ___   gr___ ___

Phonics
RF.1.3b, RF.1.3c, RF.1.3d

Parents: Your child wrote in the small box by each picture the number of the sentence that describes the picture. Then your child underlined the sentences about things he or she might like to do on a rainy day.

Read the list of things to do on a rainy day.
Put a number in each box.
Then underline the things you like to do.

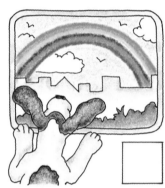

1. Cry big tears.

2. Sing a catchy tune.

3. Make a clay snake.

4. Skip in the rain.

5. Make muddy mud pies.

6. Make a yummy snack.

7. Look for a  in the sky.

8. Act very grumpy.

Phonics
RF.1.3b, RF.1.3c, RF.1.3d

Y can tell you what something is like.
What was the day like?

1. There was a lot of <u>wind</u>.
The day was

 .

2. <u>Rain</u> was coming down.
The day was

 .

3. There was a lot of <u>mud</u>.
The day was

 .

4. It felt like <u>spring</u>.

The day was

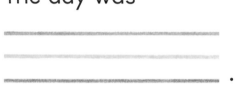

_____ .

5. The <u>sun</u> was very hot.

The day was

_____ .

6. There was a <u>nip</u> in the air.

The day was

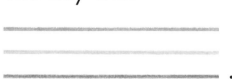

_____ .

13

1. Put an X on the first person in the leapfrog line.

2. Draw a puddle under the doll's feet.

3. Put a line under the biggest odd sock.

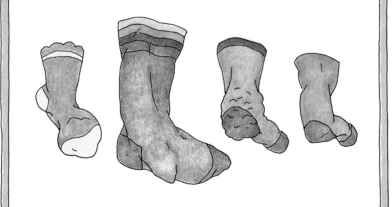

4. Put long red teeth on the monster mask.

5. Draw three beanbags in front of the dragon.

6. Make Toc dream of a candy cane.

7. Draw a blue line under the leaf print.

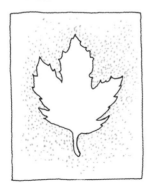

15

What to Do in Case of Rain
A Super List

From ______________________'s Brain

and then on the rest of the lines, wrote a list of things to do on a rainy day.

y + endings

fluff**y** ē

fluff**ier** ē

fluff**iest** ē

Unit 2

Parents: Your child read and traced the blue words.

1. hungr**y** ē

2. hungr**i**er ē

3. hungr**i**est ē

4. happy ē

5. happ**i**er ē

6. happ**i**est ē

17

For most words that end in *y*, change the *y* to *i* and then add the ending.

⭐ Make the y an i. Then add the ending.

sticky

stickier

stickiest

1.

muddy

4.

windy

2.

5.

3.

6.

Parents: Your child traced the blue words under the first pictures and wrote the words with -er and -est that describe the other pictures.

18

⭐ For most words that end in y, change the y to i and then add the ending.

Phonics, Spelling
RF.1.3f, L.1.2d

Parents: Your child cut out pictures and glued each one in the box with the word that describes it.

1.	2.	3.
grumpy	grumpier	grumpiest
4.	5.	6.
spotty	spottier	spottiest
7.	8.	9.
smelly	smellier	smelliest

19

For most words that end in y, change the y to i and then add the ending.

Grammar, Usage, and Mechanics
L.1.1f, L.1.4b, L.1.5d

1. funny   funnier   funniest

2. hungry   hungrier   hungriest

3. messy   messier   messiest

4. sunny   sunnier   sunniest

20

Parents: Your child drew a line from each word to the picture it describes.

For most words that end in y, change the y to i and then add the ending.

Grammar, Usage, and Mechanics
L.1.1f, L.1.4b, L.1.5d

帮助您朋友解决他们的问题

现在是制定新计划的时候了

尽量永远的微笑

因为您, 某人才快乐

休息一下吧。您工作太多了

Phonics; Vocabulary; Spelling; Grammar, Usage, and Mechanics
RF.1.3f, L.1.4, L.1.2d, L.1.2e, L.1.1f, L.1.4b, L.1.5d

Pattern Words

⭐ **Change y to i and then add the ending.**

funny

funn_ier_

funn_iest_

sunny

sunn_ier_

sunn_iest_

happy

happ_ier_

happ_iest_

angry

angr_ier_

angr_iest_

Parents: Help your child practice spelling words that follow patterns. Five of the -er and -est words will be on the Unit 2 spelling test.

Memory Words

their

now

always

because

been

Parents: Help your child memorize the spelling of these Memory Words. Each word will be on the Unit 2 spelling test.

their	now	always	because	been

Help your pals with their problems.

Now is the time to make new plans.

Try to smile always.

A person is happy because of you.

Take a rest. You have been working too much.

Then your child cut out circles and word strips to make paper fortune cookies.

22

Parents: Your child completed sentences to tell what happened in the story "The Wish."

1. The Superkids spent a day at _____

2. Oswald wished he _____

3. Oswald got stuck _____

4. A girl on a sailboat _____

What did it mean?

1. I could eat a whale!

   ○ I am very hungry.   ○ Whales are yummy.

2. I need a hand.

   ○ I want five fingers.   ○ I want some help.

3. Last one in the lake is a rotten fish!

   ○ Try not to be the last one in the lake.   ○ Kids will get fins and tails.

4. Oswald was loaded down.

   ○ He sat down.   ○ He held lots of stuff.

5. This is your lucky day.

   ○ Bad things will happen today.   ○ Good things will happen today.

6. Make a wish.

   ○ Say what you want to happen.   ○ Do difficult things.

Parents: Your child drew a line from each word to the picture it describes.

1. sleepy   sleepier   sleepiest

2. sandy   sandier   sandiest

3. messy   messier   messiest

4. I could eat a big sandwich.   I could eat a whale!   I could eat a peach.

hungry   hungrier   hungriest

Phonics; Grammar, Usage, and Mechanics
RF.1.3f, L.1.1f, L.1.4b, L.1.5d

Parents: Your child wrote Memory Words on cards, cut them out, and used them to play a game.

| been | because | their | always |

| been | now | always | their | because |

| because | their | always | now | been |

| their | because | been | now |

| always | now | been | because |

now

been

because

always   their

27

their

now

always

because

been

Parents: Your child changed *y* to *i* to write words that end in *-es* and *-ed.*

1. try

tries

tried

2. dry

es

ed

3. cry

es

ed

4. fry

es

ed

Spelling; Grammar, Usage, and Mechanics
L.1.2d, L.1.2e, L.1.1e, RF.1.3f, L.1.4c

Parents: Your child wrote the base words for the words ending in -er and -est.

1. sandiest

sandy

2. hungrier

3. fluffier

4. luckiest

5. windier

6. smelliest

29

O G F I R S T
N F T C L G R
O H U N G R Y
W O R K P A C
T N Z L I Y G
B E E N K W U
S I L L I E R
S L M A N Y X
E A S I E S T

ISBN 978-1-61436-225-8